THERE'S TREASURE EVERYWHERE

THERE'S TREASURE EVERYWHERE

A Calvin and Hobbes Collection by Bill Watterson

**Andrews McMeel
Publishing, LLC**

Kansas City

ISBN-13: 978-0-7407-7795-0
ISBN-10: 0-7407-7795-5

www.andrewsmcmeel.com

———— ATTENTION: SCHOOLS AND BUSINESSES ————

Andrews and McMeel books are available at quantity discounts with bulk purchase for educational, business, or sales promotional use. For information, write to: Special Sales Department, Andrews McMeel Publishing, LLC, 4520 Main Street, Kansas City, Missouri 64111.

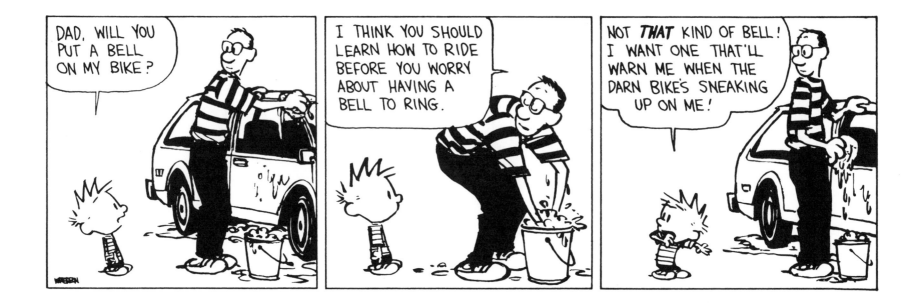

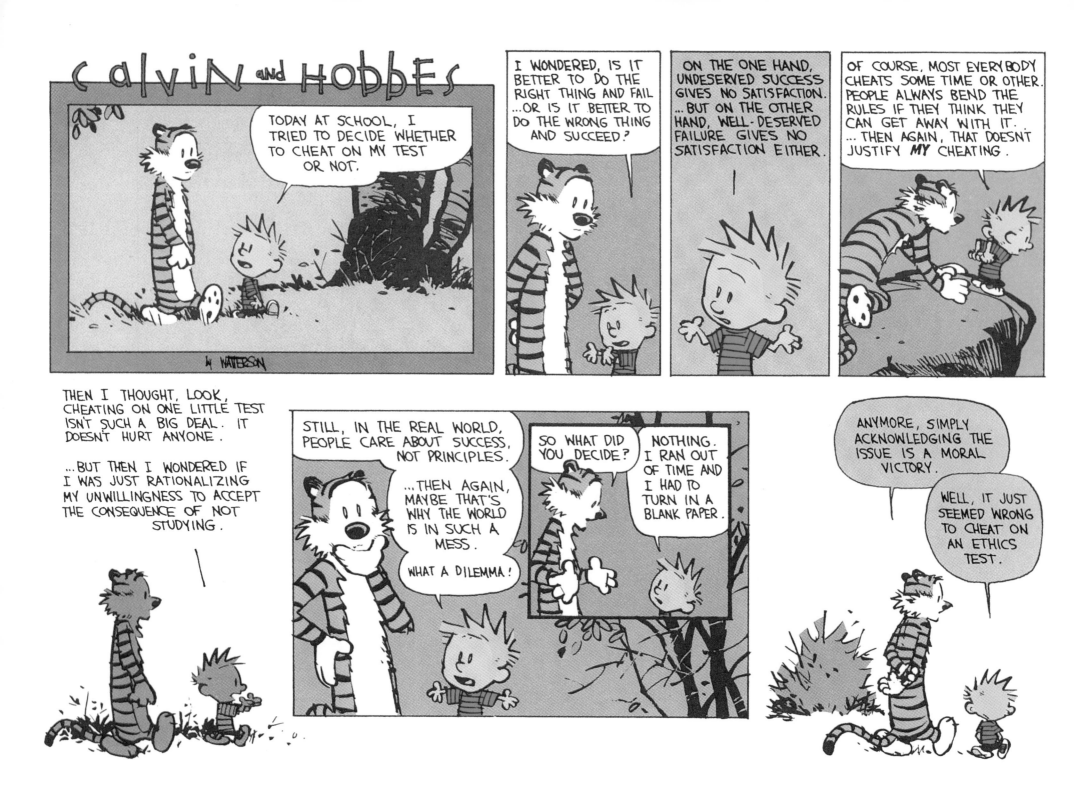

19

22

23

31

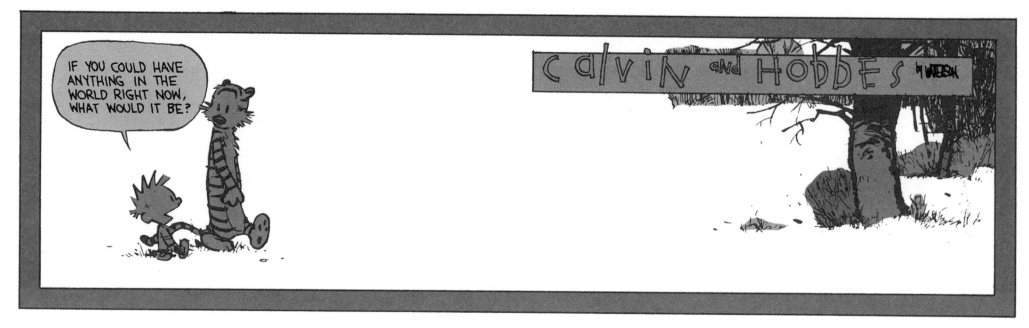

calvin and HObbES by WATTERSON

BOY, IT'S COLD OUT! IT'S A PERFECT DAY FOR US SNOWMEN!

WHAT A GREAT SPOT FOR A FEW FEET OF SNOW!

YES SIR, A SNOWMAN LIKE ME COULD BE REAL HAPPY HERE!

.. SIGHHHH...

THE DECOY ISN'T WORKING?

MAYBE DUCKS ARE EASIER TO FOOL THAN SNOW.

56

58

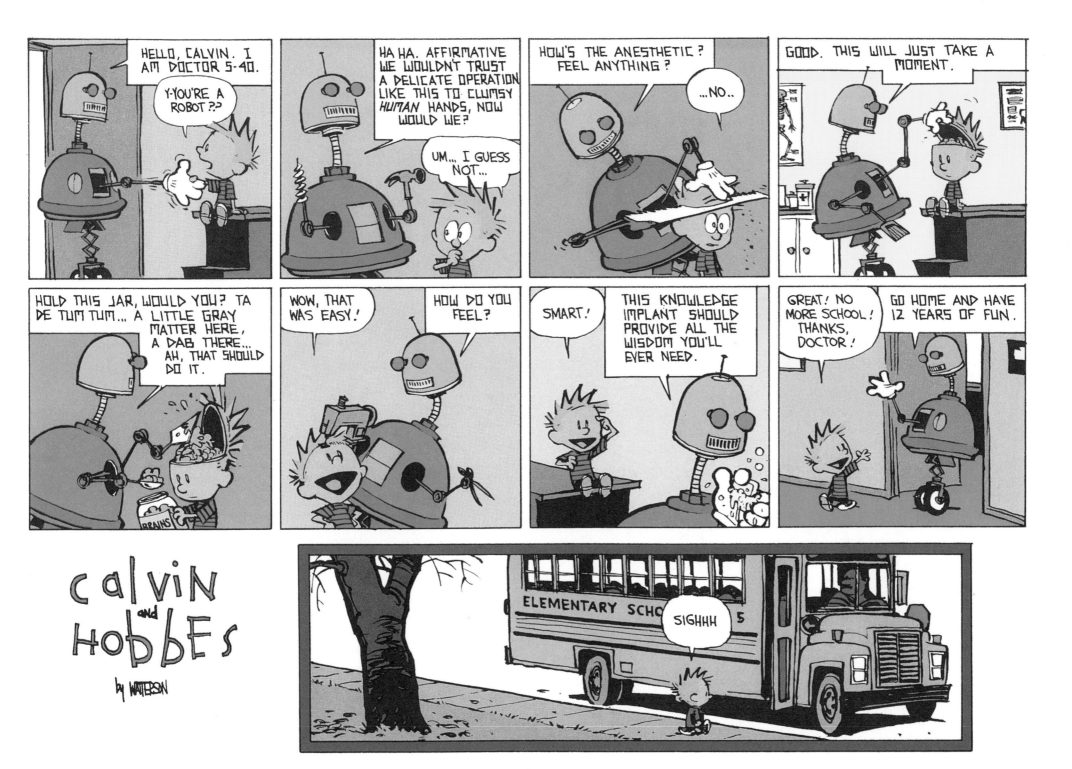

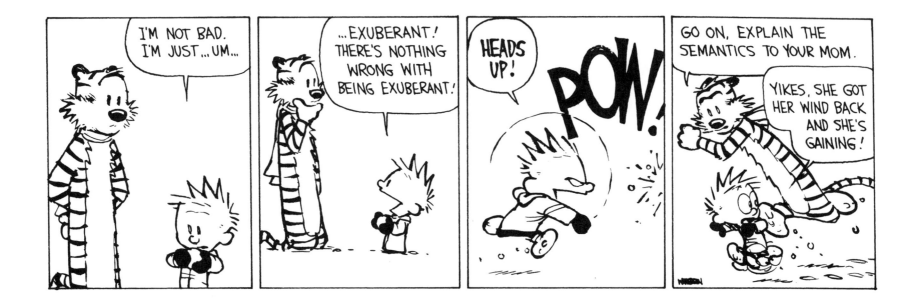

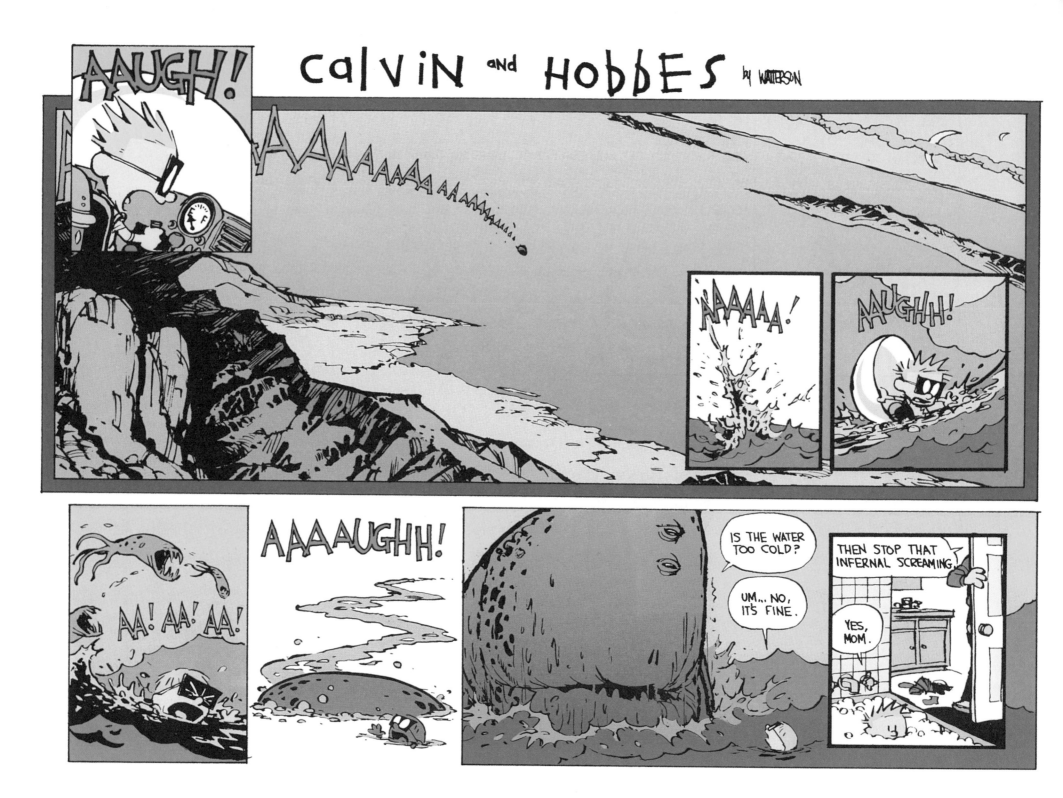

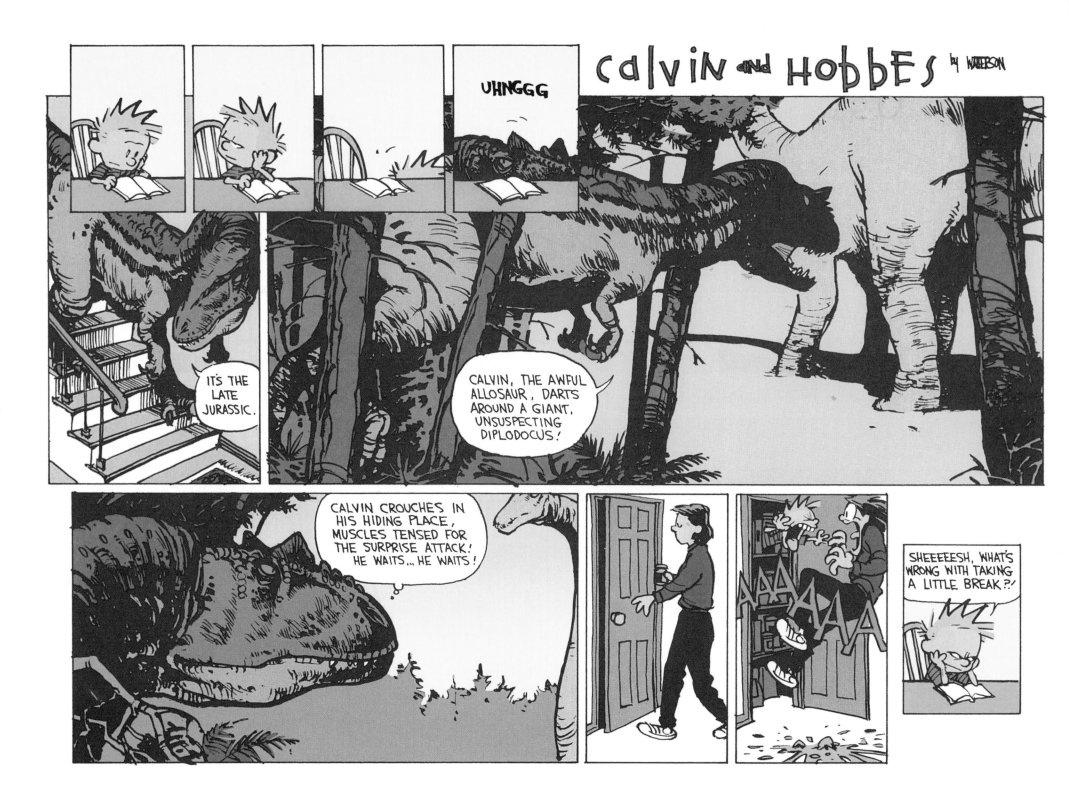

WHY IS IT THAT I CAN RECALL A CIGARETTE AD JINGLE FROM 25 YEARS AGO, BUT I CAN'T REMEMBER WHAT I JUST GOT UP TO DO?

EEP!

SCRITCH
SCRATCH
SCRITCH
SCRITCH

YOU KNOW, MOM BLAMES *ME* FOR SCUFFING UP THE FLOOR.

I WISH YOUR PARENTS WOULD TAKE OUT THESE FLOORBOARDS AND PUT DOWN SOME SOD.

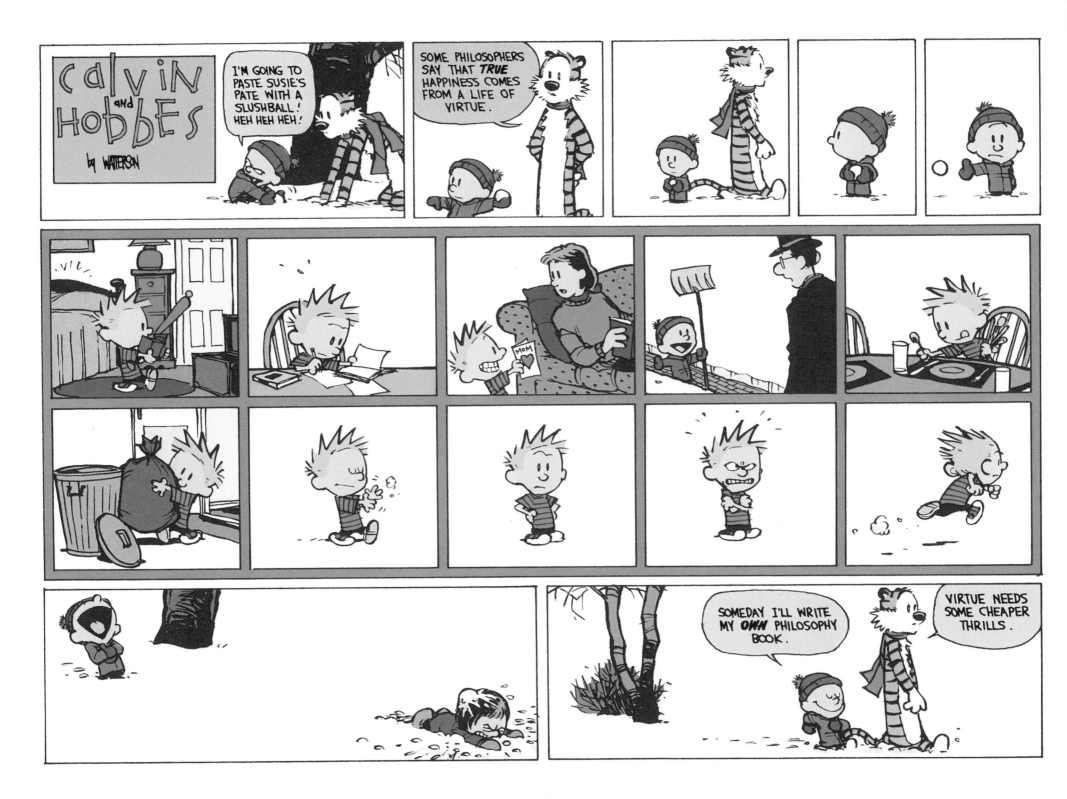

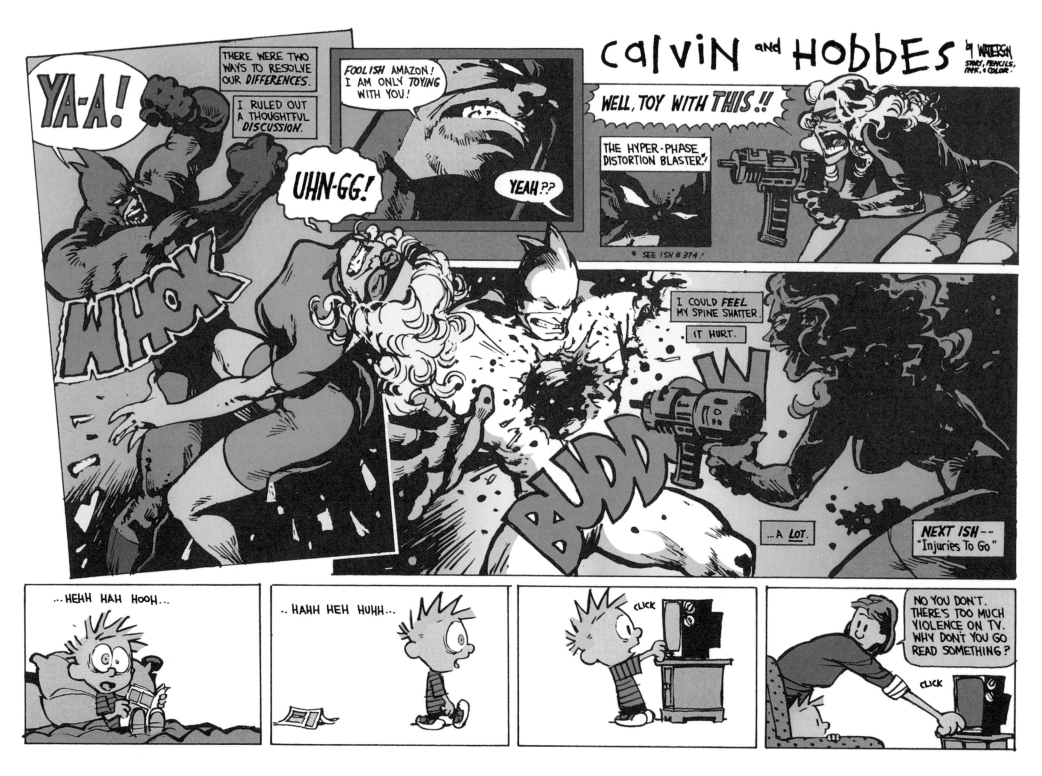

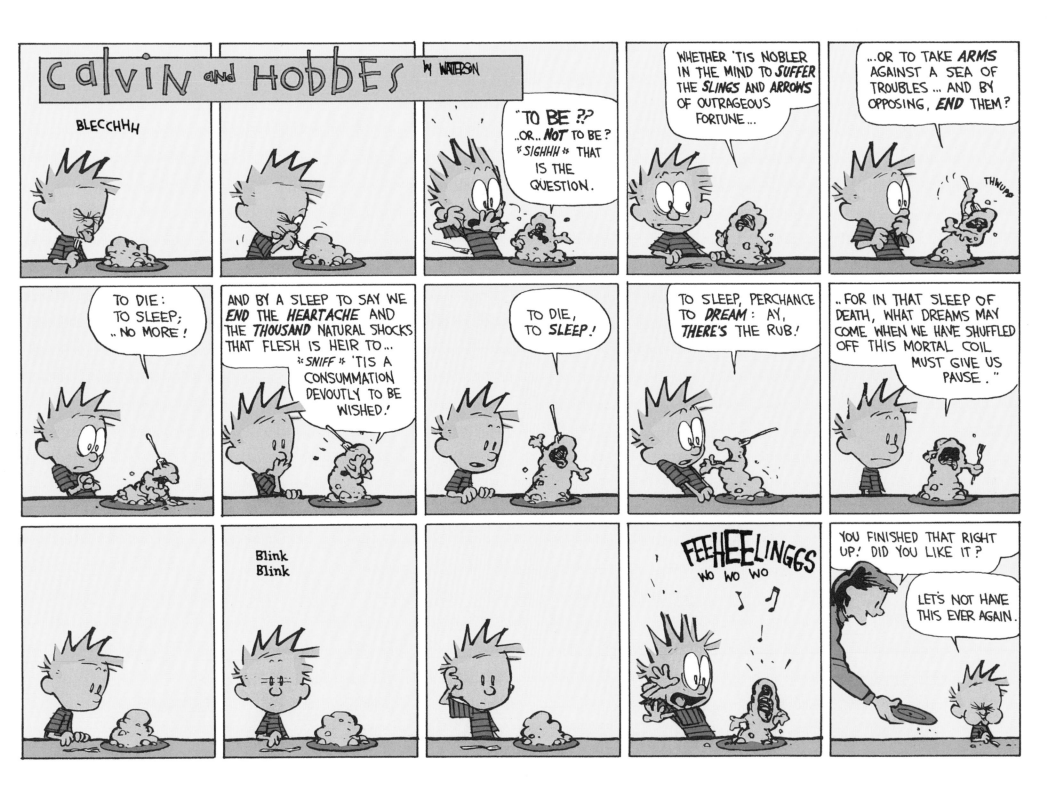

115

119

122

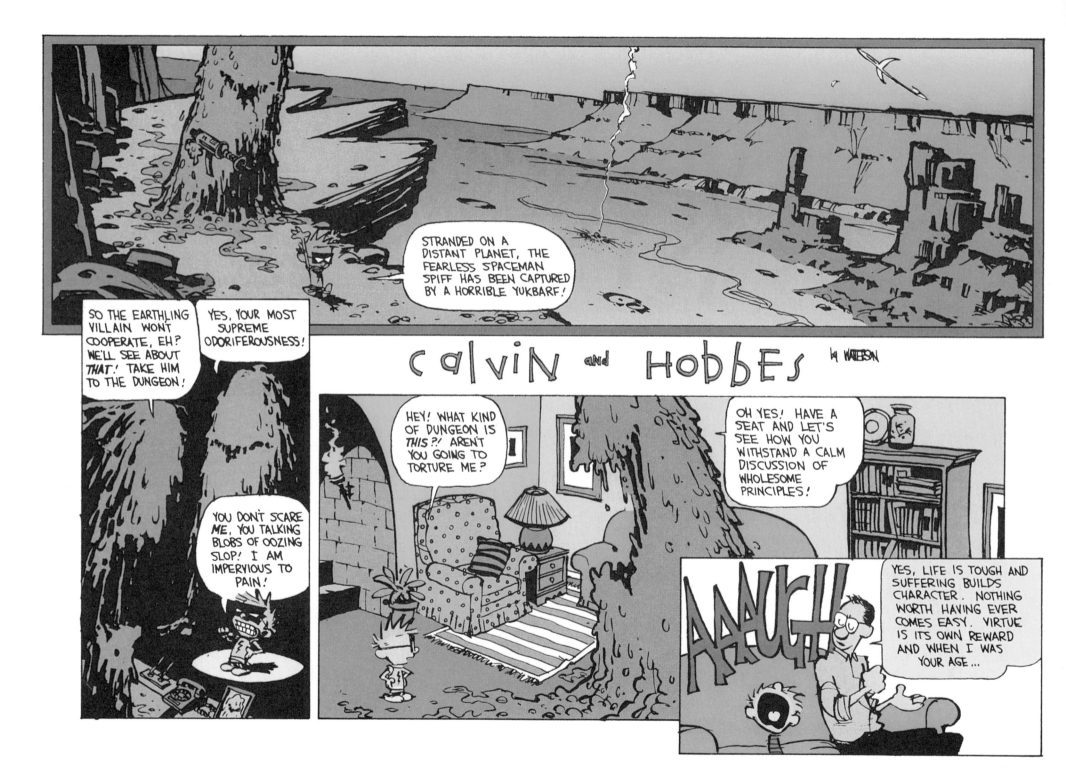

WHEN IT SNOWS, YOU CAN GO SLEDDING. WHEN IT'S WINDY, YOU CAN FLY KITES. WHEN IT'S HOT, YOU CAN GO SWIMMING.

BUT WHEN IT'S RAINING... SIGH...

..THE ONLY SPORT IS DRIVING MOM CRAZY.

I THOUGHT I HAD A GREAT IDEA, BUT IT NEVER REALLY TOOK OFF.

IN FACT, IT DIDN'T EVEN GET ON THE RUNWAY.

I GUESS YOU COULD SAY IT EXPLODED IN THE HANGAR.

I'VE HAD IDEAS LIKE THAT.

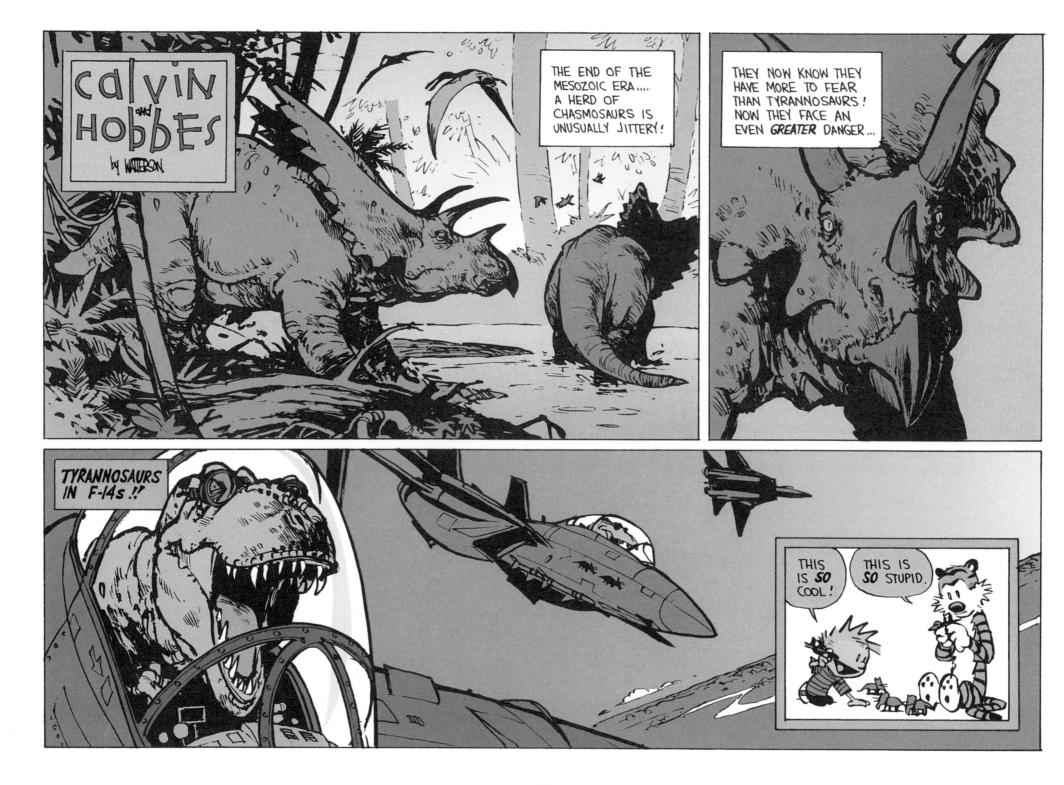

130

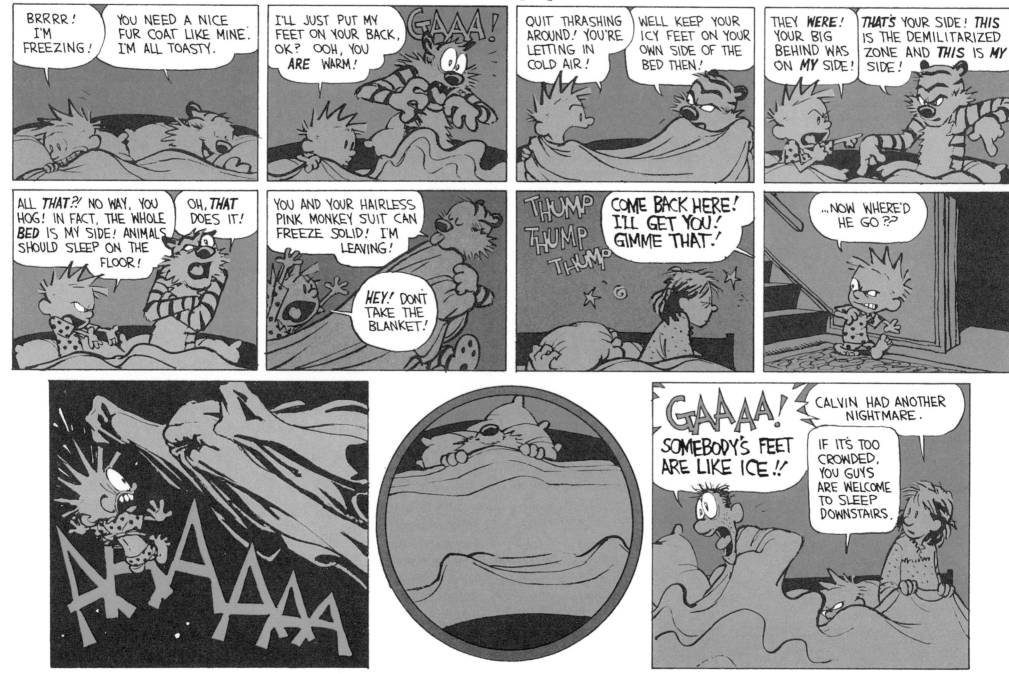

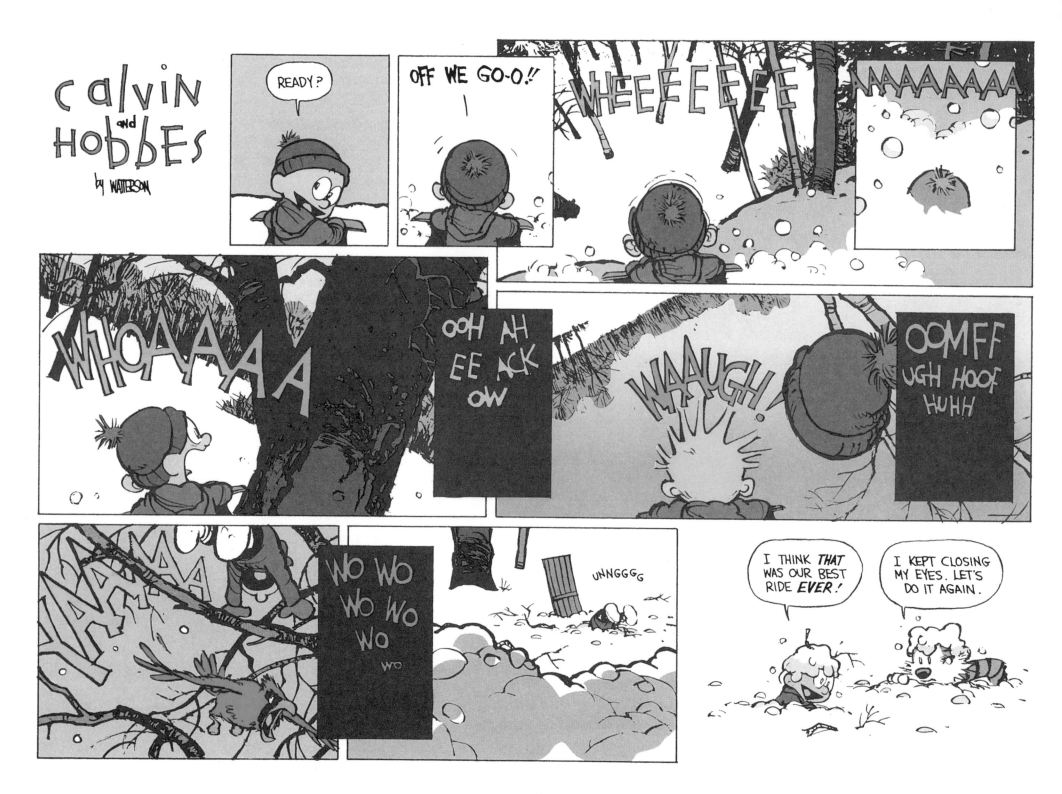

I LIKE HOMEWORK. HOMEWORK MAKES ME HAPPY.

I DON'T WANT TO GO OUTSIDE. I WANT TO DO MATH PROBLEMS.

BLEHHH

MY BRAIN ALWAYS REJECTS ATTITUDE TRANSPLANTS.

LOOK AT HOW PEOPLE ARE PORTRAYED IN COMIC STRIPS. THE WOMEN ARE INDECISIVE WHINERS, NAGGING SHREWS, AND BIMBOS!

AND THE MEN ARE NO BETTER. THEY'RE BEFUDDLED MORONS, HEAVY DRINKERS, GLUTTONS, AND LAZY GOOF-OFFS! EVERYONE IS INCOMPETENT, UNAPPRECIATED, AND UNSUCCESSFUL!

WHAT KIND OF INSIDIOUS SOCIAL PROGRAMMING *IS* THIS?! NO WONDER THE WORLD'S SUCH A MESS! I DEMAND POLITICALLY CORRECT, MORALLY UPLIFTING ROLE MODELS IN THE FUNNIES!

YES, WE ALL KNOW HOW FUNNY GOOD ROLE MODELS ARE.

AND LOOK, ALL THE KIDS ARE OBNOXIOUS BRATS!

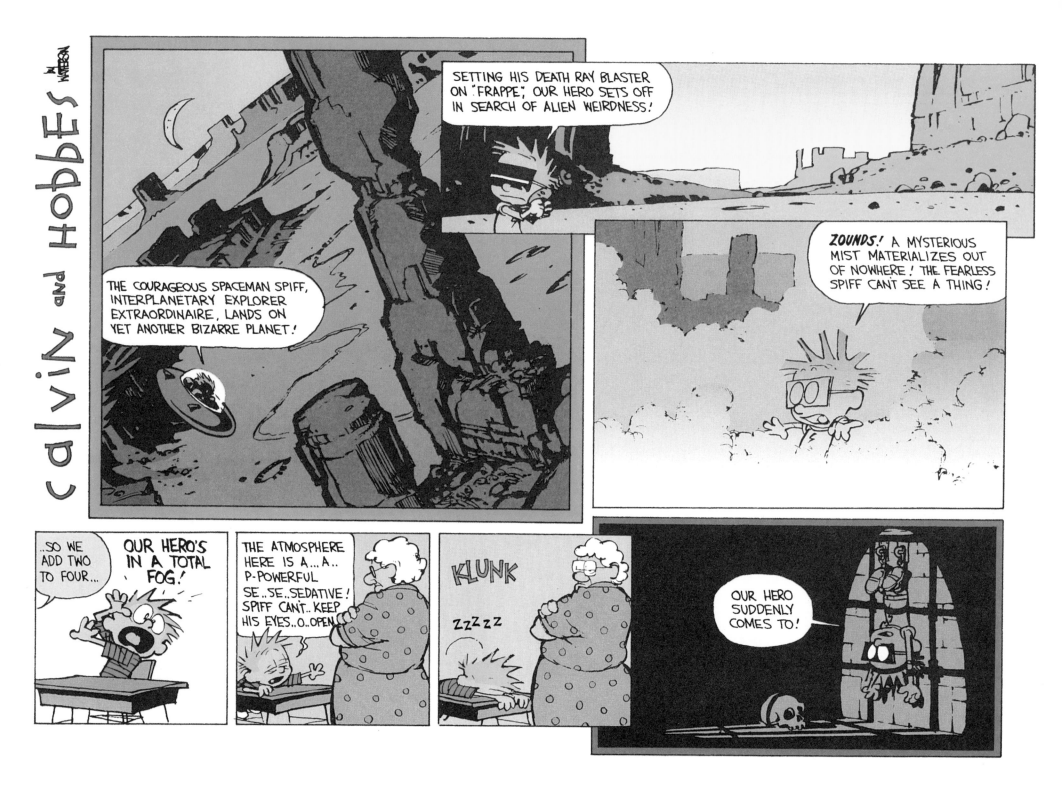

172